PEPSI-COLA
COLLECTIBLES
(with prices)

© 1990
Bill Vehling
Michael Hunt

PEPSI-COLA
COLLECTIBLES
(with prices)

Published By
L-W Book Sales
Box 69
Gas City, IN 46933

TABLE OF CONTENTS

PREFACE

Volume 1 of Pepsi-Cola Collectibles was a great success, being reprinted in 1988 with updated values. Due to many requests for a second book, we approached the publisher and was given the go-ahead.

Many pro and con statements have been made regarding Volume 1. Errors were made in Volume 1 and there are certain to be errors in this volume. Your patience and understanding are appreciated.

Volume 1 stimulated a tremendous increase in the membership of the Pepsi-Cola Collectors Club. A form to join the club can be found in the back of this book.

As with Volume 1, this book is meant to be a general guide for pricing and dating Pepsi-Cola collectibles. Prices are for near-mint items. Three factors determine the value of an item: <u>Condition</u> – condition is foremost for a serious collector; <u>Rarity</u> – it's the old principle of supply and demand; <u>Age</u> – the age of an item is the least critical of the three as some items from the 1950's are more valuable than some items from the early 1900's.

In the dating of items, some items are dated and noted as such. We tried to date the other pieces within ten years and are noted herein with the word "circa".

We have included a section in this book showing some "new or reproduction" items. Many times we have seen items offered for sale that are new or reproductions and are represented and priced as old. A word of caution: Beware! If the dealer offering a questionable item for sale will not guarantee that the item is old, then caution should be exercised.

We would certainly enjoy corresponding with fellow collectors and would appreciate hearing about any unique Pepsi-Cola items you might have. Hopefully we will be able to have a Volume III at a later date.

Thank you for buying our book. We hope you find it helpful and informative.

When wishing either of us to reply to a question, a SASE certainly would be appreciated.

Bill Vehling   Michael Hunt
P.O. Box 41233   P.O. Box 546
Indianapolis, IN 46241   Brownsburg, IN 46112

ACKNOWLEDGEMENTS

We wish to express our sincere thanks to the following without whose help this book would not have been possible.

Mr. and Mrs. Jon R. Browne
David Crook
Mrs. C. R. Davis
Jerry and Donna Dodd
Douglas Dossin
John Grasser
Mr. and Mrs. John Johnston
Terry and Dianne Mertens

With special thanks to . . .

Tom and Mary Avery – *pioneers in Pepsi collecting. We were saddened to hear of Tom's passing only weeks after photographing some of his excellent collection. Tom will be missed by all who knew him.*

Mike and Cindy Gordon – *who were just great in sharing their collection and a fine meal.*

Terry and Martha Lunt – *large contributors to this book, sending us many great photos.*

Jay and Joan Millman – *again they opened their doors for us to photograph the new additions to their fine collection, including the pocket mirror pictured on the back cover.*

Rick and Pam Russell – *who own and operate the Pepsi Parlor in Lynchburg, Tennessee, on the square. They invite everyone to stop and visit, see their collection, and enjoy the best BBQ in southern Tennessee.*

Nicholas Shepherd – *who passed away shortly after allowing us to photograph his extensive collection for Volume 1. We were saddened to hear of his passing.*

Bob and Sheri Stoddard – *who were very hospitable during our weekend visits, sharing their large and varied collection with us and taking us to some of their favorite antique places. Bob is the President of the Pepsi-Cola Collectors Club.*

Neil Wood – *our great publisher, show promoter, and friend.*

GRADING AND SIZING

Sizes: We have attempted to give accurate sizes whenever possible. Sizes are given as follows:

> Width
> Height
> Depth

When only one dimension is given it refers to length.

Colors: Most Pepsi Cola items are basically colored red, white, and blue or combinations thereof. On items where other colors are predominant they are so indicated.

Grading: **Be conservative!** The owner of an item, whether he is a collector or a dealer, tends to over-grade his particular item. Don't fool yourself!

Main factors in determining condition:
Metal items – fading or discoloration of paint, chips, scratches, dents, or rust.

Paper or cardboard items – tears, waterspotting, or other discoloration.

China or glass items – chips or cracks.

For all pieces in general be sure they have no missing parts and have not been retouched. Restoration, if done properly, in most cases will make the item appear more presentable. However, a piece that has been restored is still not "original." It should be left up to the buyer and/or owner as to whether he prefers the piece "original" or restored.

This Book Is Dedicated To The Memory Of:

Mr. Tom Avery

and

Mr. Nicholas Shepherd

ABOUT THE AUTHORS

Michael Hunt began in the antique business in 1968 as a general line dealer. He began collecting antique advertising in 1970, and started dealing in it exclusively in 1972, all part time. In 1981 he made a career decision, quitting his job and becoming a full time antique advertising dealer. He recently accepted a new position which involves traveling. His wife, Sharon, is able to travel and work with him. During the first five months in this new job, Michael was able to travel from the East coast to the West coast and back visiting Pepsi-Cola collectors, and photographing some nice collections for this book.

Sharon's lifelong drinking of Pepsi-Cola prompted the purchase of the first Pepsi item in their collection, which they still have today. The Hunts are members of the Pepsi-Cola Collectors Club and also collect a wide range of other advertising items.

Bill Vehling began collecting antique advertising after dealing in it for a few years at the local flea market. He and his wife, Amy, really enjoy looking for and finding unique pieces which they now hate to give up to sell. The Vehlings collect many different types of antique advertising including Pepsi-Cola items.

Bill Vehling is a full time dealer in antique advertising as well as a collector. His wife, Amy, teaches school and they really enjoy traveling on the week-ends and in the summer to various places in the country to search out new pieces.

The Vehlings are members of the Pepsi-Cola Collectors Club, the Cola Clan and the Tin Container Collectors Association.

Aprons

#1
Cloth Apron – 1950's
Size: 36" x 30"
Value: $45

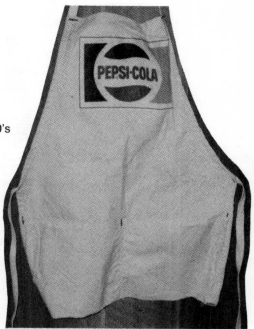

#2
Cloth Apron – 1940's
Size: 16½" x 22
Value: $75

#3
Cloth Apron – 1940's
Size: 16" x 22"
Value: $75

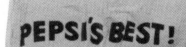

#4
Cloth Apron – 1960's
Size: 16" x 22"
Value: $35

#5
Cloth Apron – 1960's
Size: 16" x 22"
Value: $25

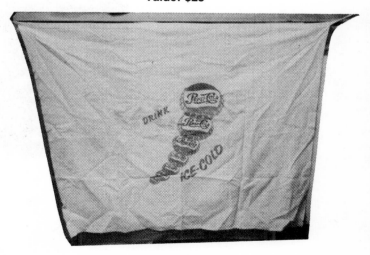

Awards

#6
Trophy – 1930's
Size: 8" x 24"
Value: $350

#7
Wall Plaque – 1950's
Size: 20" x 11"
Value: $125

Awards

#8
Trophy – Circa 1950's
Size: 10" x 16"
Value: $100

#9
Training Conference Award – 1941
Size: 12" x 10"
Value: $95

#10
Bottler's Commendation – 1950's
Size: 24" x 18"
Value: $75

#11
Bottlers Certificate – 1948
Size: 18" x 24"
Value: $45

Bottle Carriers

#12
Metal – Circa 1940's
Size: 24 Bottle
Value: $135

#13
Aluminum – Circa 1940's
Size: 24 Bottle
Value $125

#14
Tin Stadium Vendor's Carrier
Circa 1950's
Size: 24" x 7" x 12"
Value: $75

#15
Stadium Vendor's Carrier
Circa 1950's
Size: 30 Cup
Value: $75

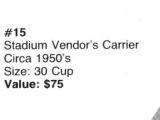

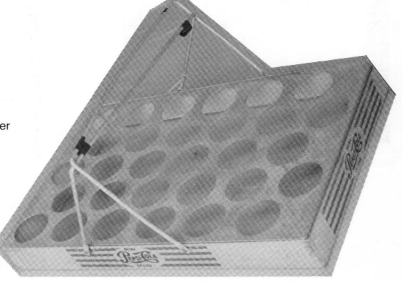

Bottle Carriers

#16
Cardboard – Circa 1940's
Size: 24 Bottle
Value: $110

#17
Wood – Circa 1930's
Size: 24 Bottle
Value: $100

#18
Wood – Circa 1940's
Size: 12 Bottle
Value: $95

#19
Wood Case (Dossin's) – Circa 1950's
24 Bottle
Value: $35

#20
Wood – Circa 1940's
24 Bottle
Value: $75

#21
Wood – Circa 1940's
24 Bottle
Value: $75

Bottle Carriers

#22
Heavy Paper – Circa 1930's
12" x 14" x 5"
Value: $125

#23
Paper – Circa 1940's
6" x 18"
Value: $80

#24
Grocery Cart – 6 Pack Holder
Circa 1950's – 10" x 10" x 8"
Value: $65

#25
Paper – Circa 1940's
8" x 10"
Value: $75

Bottle Carriers

#26
Metal – Circa 1940's
10" x 12"
Value: $135

#27
Aluminum Neck – Carrier
Circa 1930's – 6¾" x 3⅜"
Value: $125

#28
Metal – Circa 1940's
10" x 12" (6 Bottle)
Value: $125

#29
Metal – Circa 1930's
6 Bottle
Value: $90

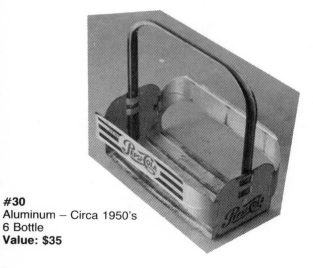

#30
Aluminum – Circa 1950's
6 Bottle
Value: $35

#31
Tin 6-Pack (White)
10" x 10" – Circa 1950's
Value: $25

Bottle Openers

#32
Metal Wall Mount with Decal
Circa 1920's – 3" x 2"
Value: $100

#33
Spinner Type (You Pay)
Circa 1910's – 3"
Value: $100

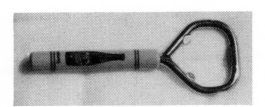

#34
Plastic Handle
Circa 1930's – 4"
Value: $95

#35
Plastic Handle
Circa 1930's – 4"
Value: $95

#36
Flat – Circa 1910's
3"
Value: $85

#37
Wall Mount (Enamel)
Circa 1940's – 2" x 3"
Value: $75

Bottle Openers

#38
Flat (Acorn Type)
Circa 1920's — 2½"
Value: $65

#39
Tin (Cap Catcher)
Circa 1940's — 3" x 8"
Value: $75

#40
Bill Tubb's Drinks
P.C. and Evervess
Circa 1940's — 3"
Value: $75

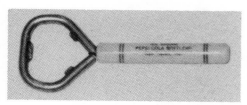

#41
Plastic Handle
Circa 1930's — 4"
Value: $65

#42
Plastic Handle
Circa 1930's — 4"
Value: $65

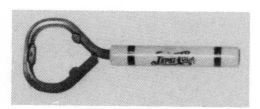

#43
Plastic Handle
Circa 1940's — 4"
Value: $55

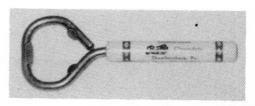

#44
Plastic Handle
Circa 1940's — 4"
Value: $55

Bottle Openers

#45
Chisel End
Circa 1920's – 4¾"
Value: $50

#46
Flat with Cap Puller
Circa 1940's – 3"
Value: $50

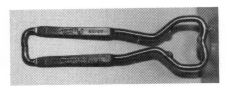

#47
Wire Type
Circa 1950's – 4¾"
Value: $10

#49
Starr X Cast Iron
Circa 1940's – 3" x 2"
Value: $50

#48
Wall Type – Circa 1950's
2" x 3"
Value: $50

#50
Wooden Handle
Circa 1950's – 4"
Value: $45

#51
Aluminum
Circa 1930's – 2½"
Value: $35

Bottle Racks

#52
Metal (Green) – Circa 1930's
24" x 40" x 15"
Value: $225

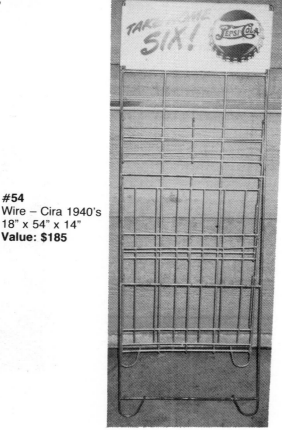

#53
Wire – Circa 1940's
25½" x 38½" x 17"
Value: $195

#54
Wire – Cira 1940's
18" x 54" x 14"
Value: $185

Bottle Racks

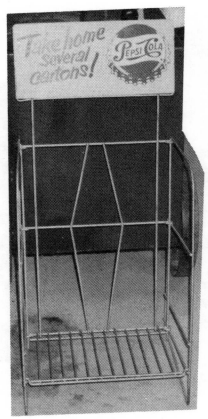

#55
Wire – Circa 1950's
18" x 40" x 12"
Value: $115

#56
Wire – Circa 1950's
12" x 54" x 24"
Value: $100

#57
Wire Rack with Tin Sign
Circa 1950's – 18" x 45"
Value: $85

Bottles

#58
Embossed – Circa 1910
24 oz.
Value: $200

#59
Paper Label – Circa 1940's
28 oz.
Value: $135

#60
Embossed (Bradham Drug Co.)
Circa 1890's – Large 2" x 5"
Value: $100 each

#61
75th Anniversary Commemerative
1973 – 6 oz.
Value: $75

#62
Paper Label – Circa 1950's
26 oz.
Value: $65

Bottles

#63
Dallas Cowboys – 1971
16 oz.
Value: $50

#64
Display Bottle (Gold Color)
Circa 1960's – 32 oz.
Value: $75

#65
ACL – Circa 1970's
16 oz.
Value: $25

#66
Paper Label – Circa 1960's
28 oz. (No Return)
Value: $50

#67
5¢ Trial Size – Circa 1970's
7 oz.
Value: $65

14

Bottles

#68
ACL – Circa 1960's
10 oz. (No Return)
Value: $45

#69
ACL – Circa 1970's
26 oz. (No Return)
Value: $20

#70
Paper Label – Circa 1970's
7 oz. (French)
Value: $15

#71
Embossed – Circa 1960's
10 oz. (No Return)
Value: $15

Calendars

#72
Heavy Paper with 12 month pad
1909 – 10" x 19"
Value: $2800

Calendars

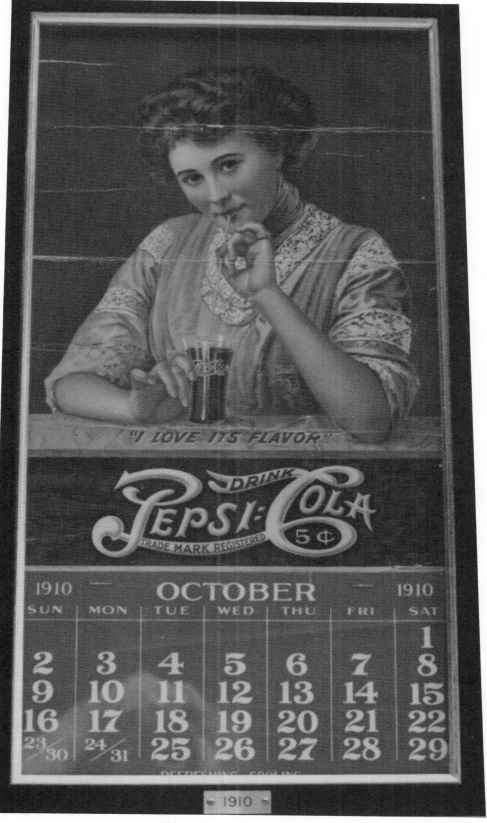

#73
Heavy Paper with 12 month pad
1910 – 10" x 19"
Value: $2800

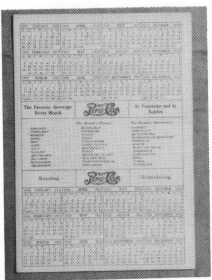

#74
Cardboard (R. Armstrong Art)
(Shows both sides)
1920 – 5" x 7"
Value: $1800

Calendars

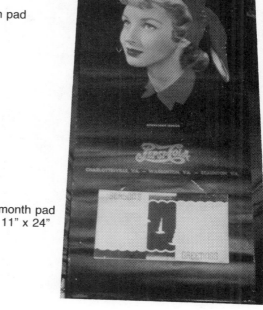

#75
Paper with 12 month pad
(N. Rockwell Art)
1949 – 15" x 40"
Value: $650

#76
Paper with 12 month pad
Circa 1940's – 11" x 24"
Value: $450

#77
Paper with 12 month pad
Circa 1940's – 11" x 24"
Value: $450

#78
Paper with 12 month pad
Circa 1940's – 15½" x 33"
Value: $450

Calendars

#79
Cardboard with replaceable pad
Circa 1930's – 9" x 12"
Value: $425

#80
Cardboard with replaceable pad
Circa 1940's – 12" x 20"
Value: $375

#81
12 Sheet – 1940
9" x 16"
Value: $350

#82
Cardboard with 12 sheets
1954 – 12" x 9"
Value: $95

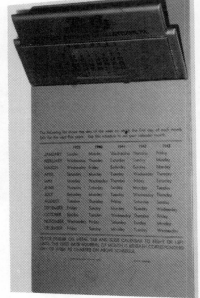

#83
Metal Clipboard with Perpetual Calendar
1939 – 6" x 12"
Value: $150

Calendars

#84
Tin – Circa 1960's
6" x 15"
Value: $35

#85
Metal – 1973
3" x 5"
Value: $25

#86
10 Sheet (Classroom use)
1979 – 14" x 22"
Value: $15

#87
10 Sheet (Classroom use)
1973 – 14" x 22"
Value: $15

Cans

#88
Tab Top (California Test Market)
Circa 1970's – 12 oz.
Value: $15

#89
Tab Top (California Test Market)
Circa 1970's – 12 oz.
Value: $15

#90
Tab Top – Circa 1960's
12 oz.
Value: $15

#91
Tab Top – Circa 1970's
12 oz.
Value: $15

#92
Tab Top – Circa 1970's
12 oz.
Value: $5

#93
Tab Top – Circa 1970's
12 oz.
Value: $5

#94
Neon with reverse glass face
Circa 1930's – 12" x 16"
Value: $3500

Clocks

#95
Neon – Circa 1930's
18" x 18"
Value: $850

#96
Neon – Circa 1930's
18" x 18"
Value: $850

#97
Neon – Circa 1940's
18" x 18"
Value: $750

#98
Tin Face – Circa 1950's
16" Diameter
Value: $325

Clocks

#99
Animated Wind-Up
Circa 1920's – 4" x 6"
Value: $850

#100
Glass Light-Up
Circa 1950's – 28" x 24"
Value: $275

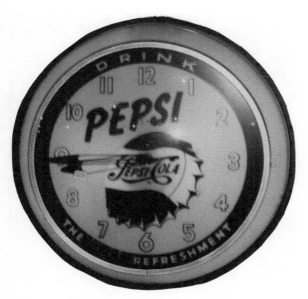

#101
Plastic and Glass Light-Up
1950's – 18" Diameter
Value: $275

#102
Tin with Wood Frame
Circa 1930's – 16" x 16"
Value: $275

Clocks

#104
Cardboard Face with Tin Frame
Circa 1950's – 16" Diameter
Value: $200

#103
Glass Light-Up
Circa 1950's
15" Diameter
Value: $200

#105
Plastic and Metal – Circa 1950's
18" Diameter
Value: $165

#106
Glass Light-Up – Circa 1940's
15" Diameter
Value: $175

Clocks

#107
Glass Light-Up – Circa 1960
15" Diameter
Value: $95

#108
Plastic Light-up – Circa 1950's
12" Diameter
Value: $150

#109
Glass / Plastic Light-Up
Circa 1960 – 18" Diameter
Value: $135

#110
Glass Light-Up – Circa 1950's
15" Diameter
Value: $95

#111
Glass Light-Up – Circa 1950's
36" x 18"
Value: $150

Clocks

#112
Glass Light-Up – Circa 1960's
16" x 16"
Value: $75

 # 113
Plastic with Metal Frame
Circa 1960's – 22" x 16"
Value: $75

#114
Plastic Light-Up – Circa 1950's
9" x 12"
Value: $95

#115
Glass Light-Up – Circa 1960's
16" x 16"
Value: $75

#116
Paper Over Wood
Circa 1960's – 28" x 12"
Value: $85

Clocks

#117
Plastic Light-Up
Circa 1970's – 30" x 30"
Value: $65

#118
Plastic Light-Up
Circa 1970's – 16" x 22"
Value: $50

#119
Plastic Light-Up
Circa 1960's – 12" x 18"
Value: $50

#120
Plastic Light-Up
Circa 1970's – 13" x 18"
Value: $40

Clothing

#121
Softball Uniform (2 Views)
1940's
Value: $300

#122
Basketball Uniform
1940's
Value: $150

#123
Driver's Coveralls
1940's
Value: $75

Clothing

#125
Shirt (Miss Pepsi)
1950
Value: $75

#124
Driver's Coveralls
1940's
Value: $75

#126
Miss Pepsi T-Shirt
(2 Views) – 1950
Value: $75

Clothing

#127
Drivers Shirt – 1950's
Value: $50

#128
Driver's Jacket – 1950's
Value: $50

#129
Cloth Vendors Hat
1940's – 11" x 16"
Value: $85

#130
Cloth Vendors Hat
Circa 1940's – 11" x 16"
Value: $60

#131
Paper Vendors Hat
1960's – 11" x 16"
Value: $15

Comic Strips

#132
Pepsi and Pete
Full Color – 1940
12" x 6"
Value: $35

#133
Pepsi and Pete
Full Color – 1940
12" x 6"
Value: $35

#134
Pepsi and Pete
Full Color – 1940
12" x 6"
Value: $35

#135
Pepsi and Pete
Full Color – 1940
12" x 6"
Value: $35

#136
Full Color
1942 – 12" x 6"
Value: $35

Coolers

#137
Glasscock Style – Circa 1930's
34" x 32" x 22" (Double Case)
Value: $900

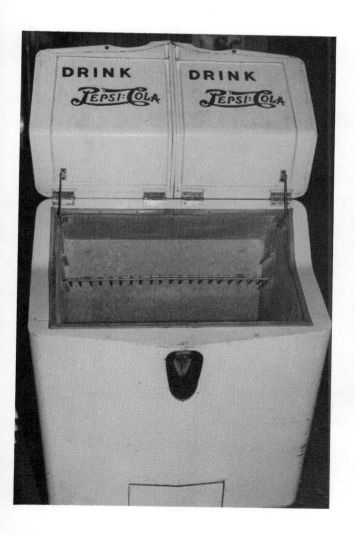

#138
Electric (2 Views)
Circa 1930's
Value: $500

#139
Electric – Circa 1940's
Value: $400

#140
Electric – Circa 1940's
Value: $375

Coolers

#141
Metal (Gray) – Circa 1940's
18" x 12" x 9"
Value: $140

#142
Metal (Silver) – Circa 1950's
24" x 19" x 13"
Value: $75

Coolers

#143
Metal – Circa 1950's
21½" x 15" x 9½"
Value: $65

#144
Vinyl – Circa 1950's
18" x 12" x 8"
Value: $40

#145
Vinyl – Circa 1950's
12" x 20"
Value: $35

Coupons

#146
Pepsi and Pete Glass Coupon
1940 – 2" x 4"
Value: $150

#147
Cooler Coupon
1940 – 4" x 2"
Value: $45

#148
World's Fair Coupon Book
1964 – 6" x 2"
Value: $40

#149
Bus Transfer (2 Views)
Circa 1940's – 1½" x 4"
Value: $35

Coupons

#150
Coupon for Silverware
Circa 1910's – 4" x 2"
Value: $35

#151
Coupon for Hygrade Water
& Soda Co.
Circa 1910's – 2½" x 1"
Value: $25

#152
Coupon for Worlds Fair
Savings Book (2 Views)
1964 – 2" x 10"
Value: $25

Coupons

#153
Playing Card
Circa 1960's – 2½" x 3½"
Value: $15

#154
Gift Certificate
Circa 1963 – 4" x 2"
Value: $15

#155
Playing Cards
Circa 1970's – 2½" x 3½"
Value: $10

#156
Coupon Booklet (Michigan)
Circa 1980's – 4½" x 8"
Value: $10

Cups and Glasses

#157
Acid Etched (Modified Flair)
Circa 1920's – 8 oz.
Value: $950

#158
Pepsi and Pete Enameled Glass
(2 Views)
Circa 1940 – 8 oz.
Value: $400

Cups and Glasses

#159
Cardboard Box and Glasses
Circa 1960's – (12) 10 oz. Glasses
Value: $75

#160
ACL – Circa 1940's
10 oz.
Value: $50

#161
Paper Cup – Circa 1940's
10 oz.
Value: $60

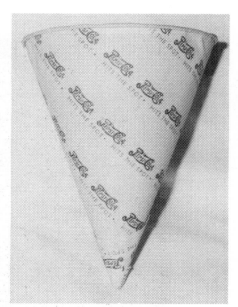

#162
Paper Cup – Circa 1930's
10 oz.
Value: $65

Cups and Glasses

#163
ACL – Circa 1960's
10 oz.
Value: $25

#164
White Ceramic Mug
Circa 1960's – 5"
Value: $25

#165
ACL – Circa 1950's
8 oz.
Value: $15

#166
ACL – Circa 1950's
8 oz.
Value: $15

Cups and Glasses

#167
Paper Cup – Circa 1940's
8 oz.
Value: $45

#168
Paper Cup – Circa 1940's
Free Sample
Value: $40

#169
Paper Cup (Pepsi Product)
Circa 1970's – 10 oz.
Value: $15

#170
Paper Cup – Circa 1950's
6 oz.
Value: $15

#171
Paper Cup – Circa 1980's
4 oz.
Value: $5

#172
Paper Cup – Circa 1970's
4 oz.
Value: $5

Desk Items

#173
Paperweight – Circa 1970's
4" x 3"
Value: $25

#174
Lucite Desk Set
Circa 1940's – 8" x 4"
Value: $100

#175
Paperweight – Circa 1960's
2" Diameter
Value: $45

#176
Ink Blotter – Circa 1930's
7¼" x 3¾"
Value: $90

#177
Paperweight
Circa 1960's – 2" x 2"
Value: $65

#178
Wooden Ruler
Circa 1960's – 12"
Value: $20

#179
Pencil Sharpener – Circa 1970's
1" Diameter x 3" Tall
Value: $15

#180
Letteropener
Circa 1970's – 8" Long
Value: $15

Dispensers

#181
Wood Barrel – Circa 1940's
50 Gallon
Value: $300

#182
Metal – Circa 1950's
12" x 16" x 17"
Value: $150

#183
Plastic & Metal
Circa 1960
Value $100

#184
Light-Up Display – Circa 1940's
13" dia. x 28" tall
Value: $1200

Displays

#185
Cardboard box for
6 Pepsi and Pete Glasses
Circa 1940's – 8" x 10" x 12"
Value: $700 (Box Only)

Displays

#186
Chalkware with Bottle
Circa 1940's – 7" x 11" x 5"
Value: $450

#187
Plastic Bottles, Cardboard 6 Pack
Circa 1950's – 16" x 18" x 6"
Value: $250

#188
Cardboard and Composition
Drummer Boy
Circa 1960's – 50"
Value: $200

#189
Cardboard House
Circa 1950's – 18" x 24" x 16"
Value: $125

Displays

#190
Santa
Circa 1970's – 48"
Value: $85

#191
Santa (Green Suit) on Reindeer
Circa 1970's – 48"
Value: $85

#192
(Not original can bank)
Circa 1960's – 12" x 12"
Value: $75

#193
Inflatible Plastic
Circa 1960's – 84"
Value: $75

Displays

#194
Witch – Circa 1970's – 48"
Value: $75

#195
Scarecrow – Circa 1970's – 48"
Value: $75

#196
Cardboard Animated
Circa 1980's – 16" x 48" x 12"
Value: $35

#197
Inflatible Vinyl
Circa 1970's – 48" Tall
Value: $35

Door Pushes

#198
Reverse Glass with Metal Frame
Circa 1930's – 4" x 12"
Value: $375

#199
Reverse Glass of Metal Frame
Circa 1940's – 4" x 12"
Value: $325

#200
Tin (Yellow Background)
Circa 1940's – 4" x 12"
Value: $250

#201
Tin – 1954 – 4" x 12"
Value: $100

Door Pushes

#202
Porcelain – Circa 1940's
30" x 3"
Value: $250

#203
Porcelain – Circa 1940's
30" x 3"
Value: $225

#204
Tin (French with yellow background)
Circa 1950's – 4" x 12"
Value: $85

#205
Tin (French with yellow background)
Circa 1950's – 4" x 12"
Value: $85

Fans

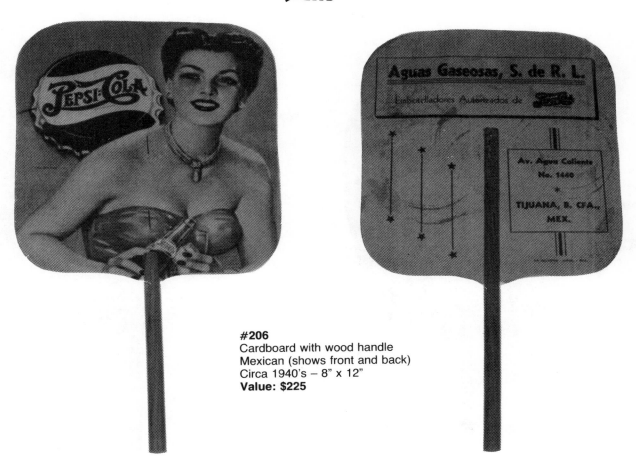

#206
Cardboard with wood handle
Mexican (shows front and back)
Circa 1940's – 8" x 12"
Value: $225

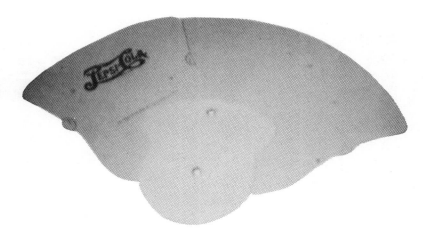

#207
Cardboard Fold-Out
Circa 1940's – 12" x 6"
Value: $90

Fans

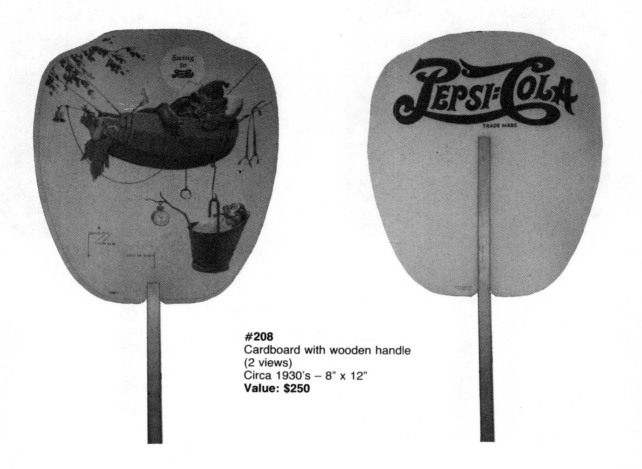

#208
Cardboard with wooden handle
(2 views)
Circa 1930's – 8" x 12"
Value: $250

#209
Cardboard with wood handle
Decatur, IL Bottling Co.
Circa 1940's – 8" x 12"
Value: $110

#210
Cardboard
Circa 1940's – 12" x 8"
Value: $100

Food Related Items

#211
Bakelite Cup Holder
Circa 1940's – 3" x 6"
Value: $150

#212
Plastic Toothpick Holder
Circa 1940's – 7" x 3"
Value: $150

#213
Picnic Pack – Circa 1950's
14" x 10" x 8"
Value: $65

#214
Glass S & P Shakers
Circa 1950's – 4"
Value: $50 Set

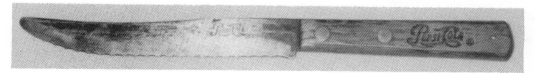

#215
Steak Knife – Circa 1940's – 8"
Value: $45

Food Related Items

#216
Pepsi and Pete Napkin
Circa 1940 – 6" x 6"
Value: $45

#218
Popcorn Bucket
Circa 1960's – 8" x 8"
Value: $35

#219
Etched Glass Plate
Circa 1960's – 7" Diameter
Value: $25

Food Related Items

#220
Glass Cruet (A.C.L.)
Circa 1960's – 2" x 5"
Value: $20

#221
Toothpick Holder
Circa 1970's – 3"
Value: $15

#222
Plastic Napkin Holder with box
Circa 1960's – 3" x 9"
Value: $15

#223
Oven Mitt – Circa 1980's
6" x 12"
Value: $15

#224
Ice Pick – Circa 1970's – 8½"
Value: $10

Jewelry

#225
Stick Pin (Enameled)
Circa 1940's – 1" Diameter
Value: $150

#226
Money Clip (Enameled)
1940's – 1" x 2"
Value: $150

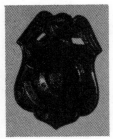

#227
Metal Security Badge
1940's – 2" x 3"
Value: $125

#228
Cufflinks (Enameled)
1940's – 1"
Value: $125

#229
Softball Medal (Enameled)
1941 – 1" x 1½"
Value: $100

#230
Belt Buckle (Tiffany)
1940's – 4" Diameter
Value: $85

#231
Cufflinks and Tie Bar
1950's – ¾" Diameter
Value: $85 Set

#232
Wristwatch – 1950's
1" Diameter
Value: $85

#233
Pearl Handled Knife
1950's – ½" x 2"
Value: $75

Jewelry, Etc.

#234
Token Holder
1940's – 1" x 1"
Value: $75

#235
Pocket Knife – 1940's – 3"
Value: $75

#236
Token (Brass)
1930's – 1"
Value: $75

#237
Money Clip – 1970's – 1" x 2"
Value: $35

#238
Charm – 1950's – 1" Diameter
Value: $35

#239
Charm (Enameled)
1970's – 1" x 1"
Value: $35

#240
Plastic Coin Holder
1950's – 3" x 2"
Value: $20

#241
Plastic Thimble
1960's – 1"
Value: $15

Letterheads, Invoices, Etc.

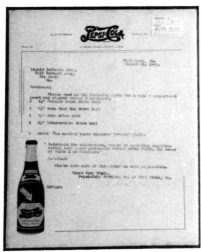

#242
Letterhead, Flat River, MO.
Circa 1930's – 8½" x 11"
Value: $25

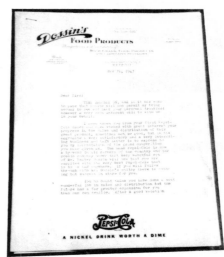

#243
Dossin's Food Products, Detroit, MI
1943 – 8½" x 11"
Value: $20

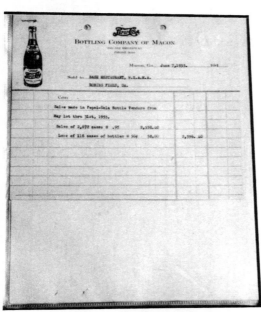

#244
Invoice, Macon, GA
Circa 1940's – 8½" x 7"
Value: $20

#245
Letterhead, Flat River, MO
Circa 1940's – 8½" x 11"
Value: $20

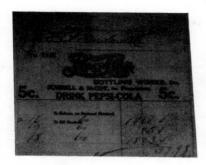

#246
Invoice
Circa 1910's – 4" x 8"
Value: $20

#247
Invoice, Macon, GA
Circa 1940's – 3½" x 7"
Value: $15

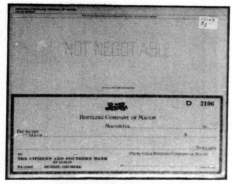

#248
Check, Macon, GA (Unused)
Circa 1940's – 8½" x 4"
Value: $15

#249
Check, Macon, GA
Circa 1940's – 8½" x 4"
Value: $15

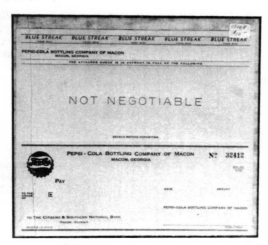

#250
Check, Macon, GA (Unused)
Circa 1940's – 8½" x 8"
Value: $15

Letterheads, Invoices, Etc.

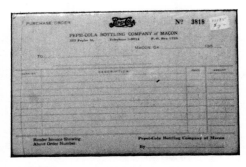

#251
Purchase Order, Macon, GA (Yellow)
Circa 1940's – 8½" x 6"
Value: $15

#252
Purchase Order, Macon, GA
Circa 1940's – 8½" x 6"
Value: $15

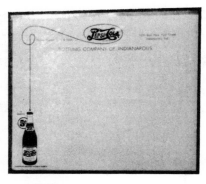

#253
Letterhead, Indianapolis, IN
Circa 1940's – 8½" x 7"
Value: $15

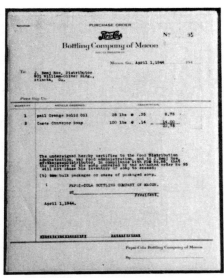

#254
Purchase Order, Macon, GA
Circa 1940's – 8½" x 11"
Value: $15

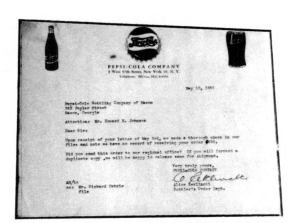

#255
Letterhead, New York, NY
Circa 1940's – 8½" x 7"
Value: $15

Letterheads, Invoices, Etc.

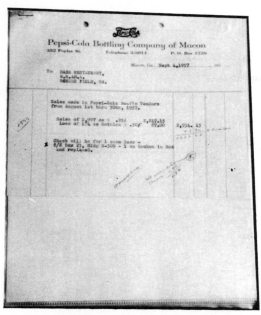

#256
Invoice, Macon, GA
Circa 1940's – 8½" x 11"
Value: $15

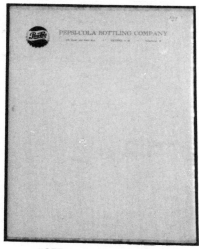

#257
Letterhead, Socorro, NM
Circa 1950's – 8½" x 11
Value: $10

#259
Invoice – Circa 1941
4" x 8"
Value: $15

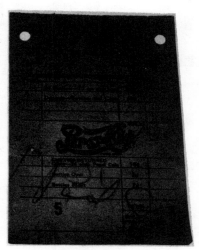

#258
Invoice, Pomona, CA
Circa 1930's – 4" x 8"
Value: $15

#260
Invoice, Macon, GA
Circa 1942 – 4" x 8"
Value: $15

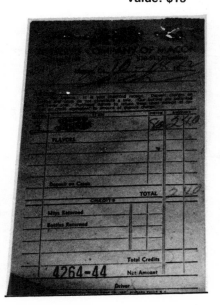

Magazine Ads

#261
2 Color – Circa 1940's
11" x 7"
Value: $15

#262
2 Color – Circa 1940's
11" x 7"
Value: $15

#263
2 Color – Circa 1940's
11" x 7"
Value: $15

#264
2 Color – Circa 1940's
11" x 7"
Value: $15

#265
2 Color – Circa 1940's
11" x 7"
Value: $15

#266
2 Color – Circa 1940's
11" x 7"
Value: $15

#267
2 Color – Circa 1940's
11" x 7"
Value: $15

Magazine Ads

#268
3 Color – Circa 1940's
6" x 14"
Value: $15

#269
3 Color – Circa 1940's
6" x 14"
Value: $15

#270
3 Color – Circa 1940's
6" x 14"
Value: $15

#271
3 Color – Circa 1940's
6" x 14"
Value: $15

#272
3 Color – Circa 1940's
6" x 14"
Value: $15

#273
Black & White – Circa 1940's
6" x 14"
Value: $10

Magazine Ads

#274
Color – Circa 1950's
11" x 14"
Value: $15

#275
Color – Circa 1950's
11" x 14"
Value: $15

#276
Color – Circa 1950's
11" x 14"
Value: $15

#277
Color – Circa 1950's
11" x 14"
Value: $15

#278
Color – Circa 1950's
11" x 14"
Value: $15

#279
Color – Circa 1950's
11" x 14"
Value: $15

Magazine Ads

#280
Color – Circa 1950's
11" x 14"
Value: $15

#281
Color – Circa 1950's
11" x 14"
Value: $10

#282
Color – Circa 1950's
11" x 14"
Value: $10

#283
2 Color – Circa 1940's
11" x 14"
Value: $15

#284
Black & White – Circa 1940's
11" x 14"
Value: $10

Magazine Ads

#285
Color – Circa 1960
11" x 14"
Value: $10

#286
Color – Circa 1960
11" x 14"
Value: $10

#287
Color – Circa 1960
11" x 14"
Value: $10

#288
Color – Circa 1960
11" x 14"
Value: $10

#289
Color – Circa 1960
11" x 14"
Value: $10

#290
Color – Circa 1960
11" x 14"
Value: $10

Magazine Ads

#291
Color – Circa 1950's
11" x 14"
Value: $10

#292
Color – Circa 1950's
11" x 14"
Value: $10

#293
Color – Circa 1950's
11" x 14"
Value: $10

#294
Color – Circa 1950's
11" x 14"
Value: $10

#295
Color – Circa 1950's
11" x 14"
Value: $10

#296
Color – Circa 1950's
11" x 14"
Value: $10

Magazine Ads

#297
Color – Circa 1950's
11" x 14"
Value: $10

#298
Color – Circa 1950's
11" x 14"
Value: $10

#299
Color – Circa 1950's
11" x 14"
Value: $10

#300
Color – Circa 1950's
11" x 14"
Value: $10

#301
Color – Circa 1950's
11" x 14"
Value: $10

#302
Color – Circa 1950's
11" x 14"
Value: $10

Magazine Ads

#303
Color – Circa 1950's
11" x 14"
Value: $10

#304
Color – Circa 1950's
11" x 14"
Value: $10

#305
Color – Circa 1950's
11" x 14"
Value: $10

#306
Color – Circa 1950's
11" x 14"
Value: $10

#307
Color – Circa 1950's
11" x 14"
Value: $10

#308
Color – Circa 1950's
11" x 14"
Value: $10

Magazine Ads

#309
Black & White – Circa 1940's
22" x 14"
Value: $20

#311
Black & White – Circa 1940's
8" x 8"
Value: $10

#312
Black & White – Circa 1940's
11" x 6"
Value: $10

#310
Black & White – Circa 1940's
22" x 14"
Value: $20

#313
2 Color – Circa 1940's
11" x 6"
Value: $10

Media Advertising Samples

#314
3 Color – 1958
8½" x 11"
Value: $15

#315
3 Color – 1958
8½" x 11"
Value: $15

#316
3 Color – 1958
8½" x 11"
Value: $15

#317
3 Color – 1958
8½" x 11"
Value: $15

#318
3 Color – 1958
8½" x 11"
Value: $15

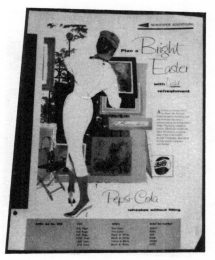

#319
3 Color – 1958
8½" x 11"
Value: $15

Media Advertising Samples

#320
3 Color – 1958
8½" x 11"
Value: $15

#321
3 Color – 1958
8½" x 11"
Value: $15

#322
3 Color – 1958
8½" x 11"
Value: $15

#323
3 Color – 1958
8½" x 11"
Value: $15

#324
3 Color – 1958
8½" x 11"
Value: $15

#325
3 Color – 1958
8½" x 11"
Value: $15

Media Advertising Samples

#326
3 Color – 1958
8½" x 11"
Value: $15

#327
3 Color – 1958
8½" x 11"
Value: $15

#328
3 Color – 1958
8½" x 11"
Value: $15

#329
3 Color – 1958
8½" x 11"
Value: $15

#330
3 Color – 1958
8½" x 11"
Value: $15

#331
3 Color
8½" x 11"
Value: $15

#332
3 Color – 1958
8½" x 11"
Value: $15

#333
3 Color – 1958
8½" x 11"
Value: $15

#334
3 Color – 1958
8½" x 11"
Value: $15

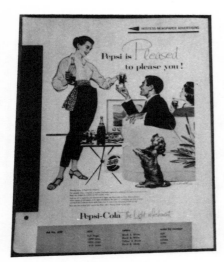

#335
3 Color – 1958
8½" x 11"
Value: $15

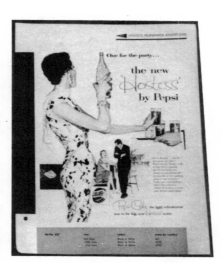

#336
3 Color – 1958
8½" x 11"
Value: $15

#337
3 Color – 1958
8½" x 11"
Value: $15

Media Advertising Samples

#338
3 Color – 1958
8½" x 11"
Value: $15

#339
3 Color – 1958
8½" x 11"
Value: $15

#340
3 Color – 1958
8½" x 11"
Value: $15

#341
3 Color – 1958
8½" x 11"
Value: $15

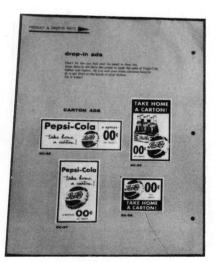

#342
3 Color – 1958
8½" x 11"
Value: $15

#343
3 Color – 1958
8½" x 11"
Value: $15

Media Advertising Samples

#344
3 Color – 1958
8½" x 11"
Value: $15

#345
3 Color – 1958
8½" x 11"
Value: $15

#346
3 Color – 1958
8½" x 11"
Value: $15

#347
3 Color – 1958
8½" x 11"
Value: $15

#348
3 Color – 1958
8½" x 11"
Value: $15

#349
3 Color – 1958
8½" x 11"
Value: $15

Media Advertising Samples

#350
3 Color – 1958
8½" x 11"
Value: $15

#351
3 Color – 1958
8½" x 11"
Value: $15

#352
3 Color – 1958
8½" x 11"
Value: $15

#353
3 Color – 1958
8½" x 11"
Value: $15

Menu Boards

#354
Wooden – Circa 1940's
14" x 32"
Value: $350

#355
Reverse Glass – Circa 1950's
12" x 26"
Value: $135

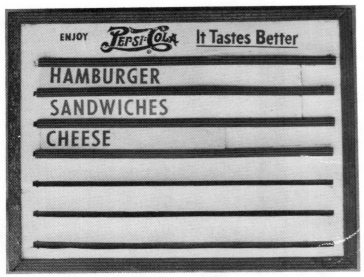

#356
Glass with Metal Frame
13" x 10"
Value: $195

#357
Plastic Light-Up
Circa 1950's – 30" x 23"
Value: $175

#358
Embossed Tin
Circa 1930's – 24" x 36"
Value: $250

#359
Tin – Circa 1930's
19½" x 30"
Value: $100

#360
Tin (Canadian)
Circa 1950's – 16" x 28"
Value: $95

#361
Reverse Glass with Metal Frame
Circa 1950's – 30" x 16"
Value: $165

#362
Glass with Metal Frame
Circa 1940's – 13" x 10"
Value: $175

#363
Plastic
Circa 1970's – 37" x 11"
Value: $25

Pamphlets and Booklets

#364
Salesman Books (LaSalle University)
Circa 1940's – 5" x 7"
Value: $65 each
Set of 5 – $375

Pamphlets and Booklets

#365
Sheet Music – 1940
10" x 8" (Open)
Value: $125

#366
Pepsi World Magazine
1940 – 8½" x 11"
Value: $75

#367
Baseball Scorecard (Los Angeles)
1941 – 8½" x 11"
Value: $65

 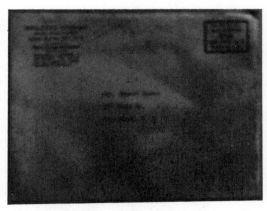

#368
Contest Consulation Notification (2 Views)
Circa 1930's – 5" x 8"
Value: $75

Pamphlets and Booklets

#369
Purity Statement
1937 – 8" x 6"
Value: $50

#370
Note Book – Circa 1910's
3" x 5"
Value: $45

#371
Pepsi World Magazine
1944 – 8½" x 11"
Value: $45

#372
Football Guide
Circa 1945 – 5" x 9"
Value: $45

#373
Program Insert
Circa 1940's – 17" x 11"
Value: $35

Pamphlets and Booklets

#374
Counter Spy Brochure
Circa 1949 – 8½" x 11"
Value: $45

#375
Informational Bulletin (2 Views)
Circa 1930's – 36" x 24"
Value: $40

Pamphlets and Booklets

#376
Football Program Centerfold
Circa 1940's – 17" x 11"
Value: $30

#377
Bottling Info. (2 Views)
1937 – 24" x 18"
Value: $30

#378
Savings Pass Book
Circa 1930's – 2" x 4"
Value: $35

Pamphlets and Booklets

#379
Machine Info.
Circa 1940's – 8½" x 11"
Value: $25

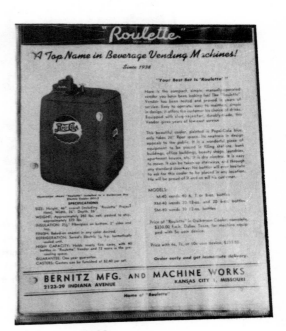

#380
Machine Info.
Circa 1940's – 8½" x 11"
Value: $25

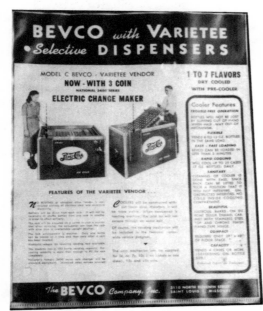

#381
Machine Info.
Circa 1940's – 8½" x 11"
Value: $25

#382
Machine Info.
Circa 1940's – 8½" x 11"
Value: $25

#383
Machine Info.
Circa 1940's – 8½" x 11"
Value: $25

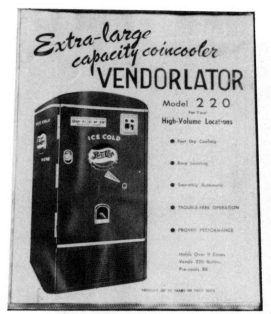

#384
Machine Info.
Circa 1940's – 8½" x 11"
Value: $25

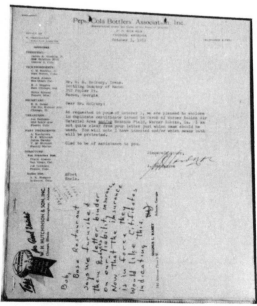

#385
Insurance Policy for Delivery Trucks
1953 – 8½" x 11"
Value: $25

#386
Animated Pencil Info.
Circa 1940's – 8½" x 11"
Value: $25

Pamphlets and Booklets

#387
Cooler Info.
1941 – 8½" x 11"
Value: $25

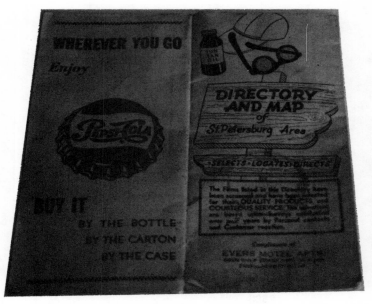

#388
Map – Circa 1950's
8½" x 11"
Value: $25

#389
Dispenser Brochure (2 Views)
1950's – 8½" x 11"
Value: $25

Pamphlets and Booklets

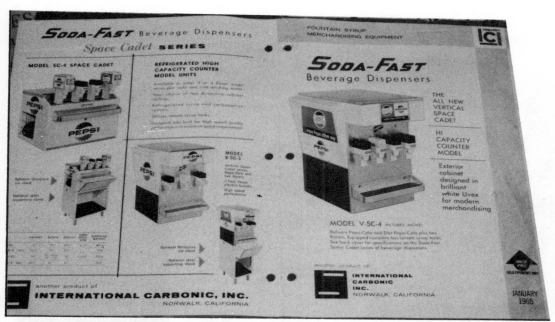

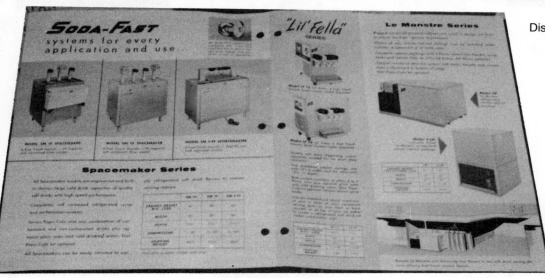

#390
Dispenser Info. (2 Views)
1965 – 17" x 11"
Value: $20

#391
Grand Opening Offer
Circa 1960's – 8½" x 11"
Value: $15

#392
Grand Opening Offer
Circa 1960's – 8½" x 11"
Value: $15

#393
Grand Opening Offer
Circa 1960's – 8½" x 11"
Value: $15

Pamphlets and Booklets

#394
Hospitacity Pack
Circa 1950's – 4" x 9"
Value: $15

#395
Wooden Case Info.
Circa 1950 – 8½" x 11"
Value: $15

#396
Hospitality Pack
Circa 1950's – 4" x 9"
Value: $15

#397
Protecta Kid Kit
Circa 1980's – 9" x 9"
Value: $10

#398
Hospitality Pack
Circa 1950's – 4" x 9"
Value: $15

#399
Service Policy for Delivery Trucks
1946 – 8½" x 11"
Value: $20

Pens and Pencils

#400
Mechanical Pencil with Bottle
Circa 1930's — 7"
Value: $145

#401
Mechanical Pencil with Bottle
Circa 1930's — 7"
Value: $145

#402
Mechanical Pencil with Bottle
Circa 1940's — 7"
Value: $125

#403
Mechanical Pencils with Floating Bottles
Circa 1940's — 6"
Value: $125 each

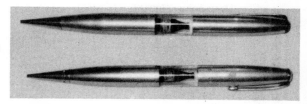

#404
Mechanical Pencil with Bottle
Circa 1940's — 7"
Value: $125

#405
Mechanical Pencil with Bottle
Circa 1940's — 7"
Value: $125

Pens and Pencils

#406
Mechanical Pencil with Floating Bottle
Circa 1940's – 6"
Value: $90

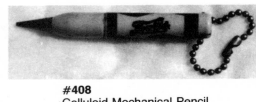

#408
Celluloid Mechanical Pencil
Circa 1940's – 4"
Value: $75

#407
Mechanical Pencil (Evervess)
Circa 1940's – 7"
Value: $90

#409
Mechanical Pencil
Circa 1940's – 6"
Value: $75

#410
Mechanical Pencil
Circa 1940's – 6"
Value: $65

#412
Mechanical Pencil
Circa 1940's – 6"
Value: $75

#411
Mechanical Pencil
Circa 1940's – 7"
Value: $65

#413
Mechanical Pencil
Circa 1940's – 6"
Value: $75

Pens and Pencils

#414
Mechanical Pencil
Circa 1940's – 6"
Value: $65

#415
Celluloid Bullet Pencil
Circa 1930's – 5"
Value: $50

#416
Celluloid Bullet Pencil
Circa 1930's – 5"
Value: $50

#417
Mechanical Pencil
Circa 1950's – 7"
Value: $55

#418
Celluloid Marker
Circa 1930's – 5"
Value: $50

#419
Celluloid Bullet Pencil
Circa 1940's – 5"
Value: $35

#420
Mechanical Pencil
Circa 1950's – 6"
Value: $40

Pens and Pencils

#421
Mechanical Pencil
Circa 1950's — 6"
Value: $40

#422
Wooden Pencil
Circa 1940's — 9"
Value: $25

#423
Ballpoint Pen
Circa 1950's — 6"
Value: $25

#424
Wooden Pencil
Circa 1940's — 9"
Value: $25

#425
Ballpoint Pen
Circa 1950's — 6"
Value: $25

#426
Wooden Pencil
Circa 1940's — 9"
Value: $25

#427
Wooden Pencil
Circa 1950's — 9"
Value: $15

#428
Wooden Pencil (2 Views)
Circa 1940's — 9"
Value: $25

Pens and Pencils

#429
Wooden Pencil
Circa 1950's — 9"
Value: $15

#430
Wooden Pencil
Circa 1950's — 9"
Value: $15

#431
Wooden Pencil
Circa 1950's — 9"
Value: $15

#432
Wooden Pencil
Circa 1950's — 9"
Value: $15

#433
Wooden Pencil
Circa 1950's — 9"
Value: $15

#434
Wooden Pencil
Circa 1960's — 9"
Value: $10

#435
Wooden Pencil
Circa 1960's — 9"
Value: $5

#436
Wooden Pencil
Circa 1960's — 9"
Value: $5

Photographs

#437
Float Muncie, IN
Circa 1930's – 48" x 36"
Value: $175

#438
Cleveland, Ohio Truck
1940's – 8½" x 11"
Value: $50

Photographs

#439
Dossin's Bottling Plant, Detroit, MI
Circa 1940's – 8½" x 11"
Value: $45

#440
Miss Pepsi on Trailer
Circa 1940's – 8½" x 11"
Value: $55

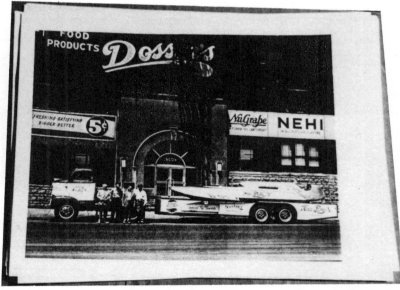

#441
Miss Pepsi
Circa 1940's – 8½" x 11"
Value: $45

Pin Backs

#442
Enamel/Metal (U.S.O. Volunteer)
Circa 1940's – 1" x ¾"
Value: $100

#443
Celluloid/Tin
Circa 1940's – 1½" Diameter
Value: $75

#444
Celluloid/CDBD with Ribbon
Circa 1940's – 2½" Diameter
Value: $75

#445
Celluloid/Tin
Circa 1940's – 2½" Diameter
Value: $65

#446
Celluloid/Tin
Circa 1950's – 2½" x 2½"
Value: $50

#447
Celluloid/Tin
3½" Diameter – Circa 1960's
Value: $35

#448
Celluloid/Tin
Circa 1950's – 3½" Diameter
Value: $35

#449
Celluloid/Tin
Circa 1950's – 1" Diameter
Value: $30

#450
Celluloid/Tin
Circa 1950's – 2" Diameter
Value: $30

Pinbacks

#451
Celluloid/Tin
Circa 1950's – 2½" x 2½"
Value: $30

#452
Celluloid/Tin
Circa 1950's – 2" Diameter
Value: $30

#453
Celluloid/Tin
Circa 1940's – 1" Diameter
Value: $25

#454
Celluloid/Tin
Circa 1950's – 1" Diameter
Value: $25

#455
Celluloid/Tin
Circa 1960 – 2½" Diameter
Value: $25

#456
Celluloid/Tin
Circa 1960's – 2½" Diameter
Value: $25

#457
Celluloid/Tin
Circa 1960's – 2½" Diameter
Value: $25

#458
Celluloid/Tin (G.O.P.)
1964 – 2½" Diameter
Value: $25

#459
Celluloid/Tin
Circa 1960's – 2½" Diameter
Value: $20

Pinbacks

#460
Madison, IN Regatta
1969 – 2½" Diameter
Value: $15

#461
Madison, IN Regatta
1968 – 2½" Diameter
Value: $15

#462
Madison, IN Regatta
1964 – 2½" Diameter
Value: $25

#463
Madison, IN Regatta (Child Admission)
1969 – 2½" Diameter
Value: $25

#464
Madison, IN Regatta
1965 – 2½" Diameter
Value: $20

#465
Celluloid/Tin
Circa 1960's – 2½" Diameter
Value: $20

#466
Celluloid/Tin
Circa 1960's – 2½" Diameter
Value: $20

#467
Celluloid/Tin
Circa 1960's – 2" Diameter
Value: $15

#468
Celluloid/Tin
Circa 1960's – 2½" Diameter
Value: $20

#469
Celluloid/Tin
Circa 1970's – 2½" x 1"
Value: $10

Records

#470
Record with Mailing Folder
Circa 1940's
Value: $65

#471
Circa 1960's
Value: $20

#472
Circa 1960's
Value: $45

#473
Radio Transcriptions
Circa 1962 – 33⅓ R.P.M.
Value: $25

#474
Back Bar Festoon
Circa 19450's
Value: $1400

#475
Framed Trolley Sign
Yellow background (Canadian)
Circa 1940's – 22" x 12"
Value: $325

Cardboard Signs

#476
Trolley Sign – Yellow background
Circa 1940 – 21" x 11"
Value: $1200

#477
Trolley Sign – Yellow background
Circa 1940 – 21" x 11"
Value: $1400

Cardboard Signs

#478
Trolley Sign
Circa 1940's – 28" x 11"
Value: $225

#479
Trolley Sign
Circa 1940's – 28" x 11"
Value: $175

#480
Trolley Sign
Circa 1940's – 28" x 11"
Value: $175

Cardboard Signs

#481
Trolley Sign
Circa 1940's – 28" x 11"
Value: $200

#482
Trolley Sign
Circa 1940's – 28" x 11"
Value: $175

#483
Trolley Sign
Circa 1950's – 28" x 11"
Value: $35

#484
Trolley Sign with original frame
Circa 1970's – 28" x 11"
Value: $45

Cardboard Signs

#485
Trolley Sign
Circa 1950's – 28" x 11"
Value: $50

#486
Trolley Sign
Circa 1970's – 28" x 11"
Value: $15

#487
Trolley Sign
Circa 1970's – 28" x 11"
Value: $15

#488
Trolley Sign
Circa 1970's – 28" x 11"
Value: $15

Cardboard Signs

#489
Channel Sign
Circa 1940's – 20" x 8"
Value: $125

#490
Die Cut – Circa 1940's
12" x 18"
Value: $300

#491
Original Frame
Circa 1940's – 28" x 11"
Value: $275

#492
Die Cut – Circa 1940's
10" x 16"
Value: $100

#493
Blue – Circa 1920's
13½" x 5½"
Value: $350

Cardboard Signs

#495
Hanger – Circa 1940's
12" x 6"
Value: $210

#494
Die Cut – Circa 1930's
10" x 32"
Value: $250

#496
3-D Easel Back – Die Cut
Circa 1940's – 20" x 20"
Value: $250

#497
Die Cut/Easel Back
Circa 1950's – 14" x 36"
Value: $225

Cardboard Signs

#498
Easel Back
Circa 1930's – 5" x 16"
Value: $190

#499
Die Cut – Heavy Cardboard
Circa 1950's – 30" x 12"
Value: $75

#500
Die Cut – Display Sign
Circa 1940's – 8" x 14"
Value: $125

#501
Die Cut – Easel Back
Circa 1950's – 16" x 20"
Value: $95

Cardboard Signs

#502
Self-Framed
Circa 1940's – 27" x 21½"
Value: $175

#503
3-D Easel Back
Circa 1950's – 17" x 20"
Value: $45

#504
Die Cut – Easel Back
Circa 1950's – 16" x 20"
Value: $65

#505
3-D Easel Back
Circa 1950's – 16" x 20"
Value: $65

Cardboard Signs

#506
Self-Framed
Circa 1950's – 26" x 20"
Value: $110

#507
Easel-Back
Circa 1960's – 8" x 12"
Value: $45

#508
Self-Framed
Circa 1950's – 20" x 20"
Value: $95

#509
Circa 1940's
24" x 26"
Value: $500

#510
Green Background – Embossed
6" x 4"
Value: $325

#511
Circa 1940's – 16" x 14"
Value: $225

Cardboard Signs

PEPSI's BEST
Take No Less

#512
Poster
Circa 1940's – 37" x 25"
Value: $150

#513
Poster
Circa 1950's – 38" x 28"
Value: $60

Be Sociable, Have a
Pepsi

#514
Poster
Circa 1950's – 38" x 28"
Value: $55

Cardboard Signs

#515
Scoreboard (2 Views)
Circa 1930's – 13" x 30"
Value: $375

#516
Circa 1940's – 18" x 12"
Value: $225

#517
Poster
Circa 1950's – 38" x 28"
Value: $55

#518
Circa 1930's
36" Diameter
Value: $350

Cardboard Signs

#519
Wall Hanger
(Yellow background/Canadian)
Circa 1940's – 8" x 14"
Value: $250

#520
Bottle Holder – Foil Covered
Circa 1930's – 5" x 18"
Value: $110

#521
Bottle Holder – Foil Covered
Circa 1930's – 5" x 18"
Value: $110

#522
Hanger
Circa 1940's – 15" x 15"
Value: $325

#523
2 Sided Fan Hanger
Circa 1940's – 4" x 7"
Value: $325

Cardboard Signs

#524
Amortization Calculator
Circa 1940's – 10" Diameter
Value: $65

#525
Circa 1940's – 16" x 14"
Value: $225

#526
Circa 1940's – 18" x 12"
Value: $225

#527
Basketball Schedule
(Yellow Background)
Circa 1974 – 14" x 20"
Value: $20

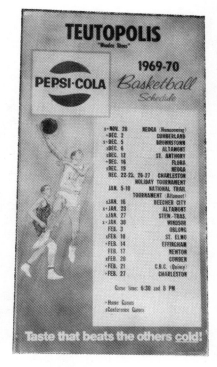

#528
Basketball Schedule
Circa 1972 – 14" x 20"
Value: $20

#529
Basketball Schedule
Circa 1969 – 14" x 20"
Value: $25

Cardboard Signs

#530
Circa 1940
14" x 10"
Value: $150

#531
Basketball Schedule
(Yellow background)
Circa 1967 – 14" x 20"
Value: $25

#532
Basketball Schedule
Circa 1982 – 14" x 20"
Value: $15

#533
Canadian
Circa 1940's – 13" x 14"
Value: $75

Cardboard Signs

#534
Framed – Circa 1940's
34½" x 19½"
Value: $125

#535
Basketball Schedule
Circa 1981 – 14" x 20"
Value: $15

#536
Foil Covered
Circa 1950's – 8" x 3"
Value: $25

#537
Corrugated (Yellow background)
Circa 1950's – 57" x 30"
Value: $55

#538
Circa 1950's — 14" x 18"
Value: $45

#539
Circa 1960's — 24" x 36"
Value: $25

#540
Basketball Schedule
Circa 1962 — 14" x 20"
Value: $35

#541
Basketball Schedule
Circa 1973 — 14" x 20"
Value: $20

Glass Signs

#542
Reverse Glass with Wood Frame
Circa 1940's – 12" x 8"
Value: $450

#543
Reverse Glass with Metal Frame
Circa 1958-1963 – 14" x 14"
Value: $85

#544
Glass Mirror
Circa 1950's – 6" x 11"
Value: $100

#545
Leaded Glass
Circa 1970's – 18" x 14"
Value: $65

Light-Up Signs

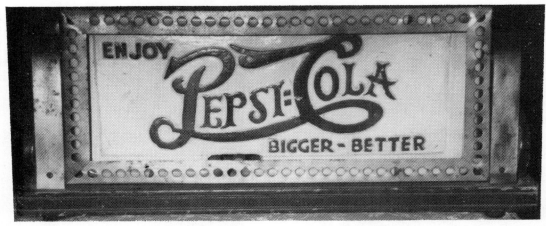

#546
Neon with Metal and Wood Frame
Circa 1930's — 14" x 8"
Value: $1500

#547
Neon — Circa 1940's
24" x 18"
Value: $1200

#548
Glass, Metal Frame, with
Revolving Light
Circa 1930's — 16" x 10"
Value: $850

Light-Up Signs

#549
Plastic Front Metal Frame
Revolving Cylinder
Circa 1950's – 20½" x 10" x 7½"
Value: $350

#550
Plastic Revolving
Circa 1950's – 30" x 18"
Value: $225

#551
Neon
Circa 1960's – 18" x 10"
Value: $200

#552
Reverse Glass and Mirror
Circa 1950's – 12" x 12"
Value: $165

#553
Plastic – Circa 1960's
48" x 10"
Value: $165

Light-Up Signs

#554
Plastic with Metal Frame
Circa 1950's – 30" x 12"
Value: $150

#555
Plastic Revolving
Circa 1970's – 18" x 14"
Value: $150

#556
Plastic
Circa 1950's – 24" x 10"
Value: $150

#557
3-D Plastic
Circa 1950's – 12" x 26"
Value: $125

#558
Plastic
Circa 1960's – 24" x 16"
Value: $150

Light-Up Signs

#559
Plastic
Circa 1950's – 12" x 8"
Value: $150

#560
Plastic
Circa 1950's – 14" x 6"
Value: $110

#562
Plastic
Circa 1960's – 10" x 10"
Value: $60

#561
Plastic with Metal Frame
Circa 1950's
9" x 12" x 5"
Value: $75

#563
Plastic Shade with Can Base
Circa 1970's
14" Diameter – 18" Tall
Value: $30

#564
The Pepsi-Cola Girl
(R. Armstrong Art)
Circa 1919 – 14½" x 18"
Value: $1800

#565
Paper Banner
Circa 1940 – 42" x 76"
Value: $1500

Paper Signs

#566
Paper – Pictures Foil Covered Bottle
Circa 1934 – 16" x 12"
Value: $750

#567
Die Cut Paper – Uncut Set
Circa 1940's – 6" x 18"
Value: $650

Paper Signs

#568
Machine Stick-On
Circa 1950's – 12" x 8"
Value: $35

#570
Circa 1950's – 18" x 24"
Value: $60

#569
Window Decal
Circa 1950's – 10" x 8"
Value: $25

#571
Window Decal (Yellow background)
Circa 1950's – 10" x 8"
Value: $20

Paper Signs

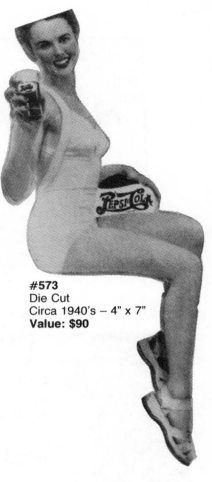

#572
Die Cut
Circa 1940's – 4" x 7"
Value: $90

#573
Die Cut
Circa 1940's – 4" x 7"
Value: $90

#574
Die Cut
Circa 1940's – 4" x 7"
Value: $90

#575
Die Cut
Circa 1940's – 4" x 7"
Value: $90

Paper Signs

#576
Heavy Paper
Circa 1940's – 24" x 36"
Value: $400

577
Paper Window Sign
Circa 1930's – 11" x 7½"
Value: $225

#578
Paper Banner
Circa 1950's – 28" x 11"
Value: $90

#579
Armed Forces Insignia (B & W)
Circa 1940's – 18" x 24"
Value: $150

Paper Signs

#580
Paper Banner
Circa 1940's – 28" x 11"
Value: $185

#581
Paper Window Sign
Circa 1950's – 18" x 10"
Value: $150

#582
Circa 1940's – 20" x 8"
Value: $65

#583
Chinese Lantern
Circa 1950's – 12" Diameter
Value: $125

#584
Original Artist Painting
Circa 1950's – 36" x 14"
Value: $225

Plastic Signs

#585
3-D Plastic/Cardboard
Circa 1950's – 24" x 28½"
Value: $110

#586
Heavy Plastic
Circa 1970's – 26" Diameter
Value: $100

#587
3-D
Circa 1960's
14" x 10"
Value: $75

#588
3-D
Circa 1960's
18" x 12"
Value: $50

#589
3-D
Circa 1960's
11" x 14½"
Value: $50

#590
3-D
Circa 1960's
16" x 14"
Value: $50

#591
3-D
Circa 1960's
11½" x 14½"
Value: $50

#592
Circa 1960's
12" x 18"
Value: $35

Plastic Signs

#593
Plastic/Cardboard
Circa 1950's – 12" x 6"
Value: $45

#594
Concave with Wood Frame
Circa 1970's – 20" x 20"
Value: $35

#595
Fanhanger with CDBD Insert
Circa 1950's – 3" Diameter
Value: $35

#597
Wood Grain – Circa 1970's
11½" x 9" x 1"
Value: $20

#596
3-D
Circa 1960's
7" x 17"
Value: $35

Porcelain Signs

#598
Circa 1940's – 18" x 44"
Value: $600

#599
Circa 1940's
30" x 10"
Value: $475

#600
Circa 1940's
56" x 31"
Value: $375

#601
Circa 1940's
24" x 36"
Value: $375

Porcelain Signs

#603
Yellow Background
Circa 1950's – 33" x 22"
Value: $175

#602
Circa 1940's
16" Diameter
Value: $250

#604
Convex
Circa 1950's
48" Diameter
Value: $175

#605
Circa 1950's
40" x 40"
Value: $165

Porcelain Signs

#606
Yellow background
Circa 1950's – 29" x 12"
Value: $110

#607
Yellow background
Circa 1950's – 29" x 12"
Value: $100

#608
2 Sided Flange (Canadian)
Circa 1950's – 15" x 13"
Value: $100

#609
Yellow and brown
Circa 1960's – 29" x 11"
Value: $100

Tin Signs

#610
Embossed – Circa 1940's
62" x 45"
Value: $250

#611
Embossed/green background
Circa 1910's – 30" x 20"
Value: $1000

#612
Embossed aluminum
Circa 1940's – 22" x 46"
Value: $250

#613
Embossed/green
Circa 1910's – 8" x 3"
Value: $350

Tin Signs

#614
Yellow background (Canadian) embossed
Circa 1930's – 36" x 24"
Value: $450

#615
Embossed
Circa 1940's – 50" x 36"
Value $225

#616
Embossed
Circa 1930's – 40" x 12"
Value: $225

Tin Signs

#617
Die Cut
Circa 1930's – 12" x 45"
Value: $325

#618
Die Cut – Circa 1930's
12" x 45"
Value: $400

#619
Die Cut – Circa 1940's
12" x 45"
Value: $225

#620
Die Cut – Circa 1930's
8" x 29½"
Value: $300

#621
Die Cut – Circa 1940's
8" x 29½"
Value: $225

#622
3-D – Circa 1940's
31" Diameter
Value: $350

#622
3-D
Circa 1940's
31" Diameter
Value: $350

#623
Embossed – Circa 1950's
18" Diameter
Value: $125

#624
Embossed 3-D
Circa 1950's – 24" Diameter
Value: $125

#625
Embossed
Circa 1950's – 18" Diameter
Value: $125

Tin Signs

#626
Flange 2 sided
Circa 1930's – 20" Diameter
Value: $275

#627
Die Cut School Crossing
Sign (Both Sides Shown)
Circa 1950's – 24" x 60"
Value: $275

#628
French – Yellow Background
2 Sided Flange
Circa 1940's – 24" x 24"
Value: $165

Tin Signs

#630
Rack Sign
Circa 1930's – 24" x 4"
Value: $125

#629
Flange/2 Sided
Circa 1950's – 12" Diameter
Value: $125

#631
Rack Sign/Yellow Background
Circa 1930's – 24" x 14"
Value: $85

#632
Rack Sign
Circa 1950's – 18" Diameter
Value: $75

#633
Rack Sign
Circa 1940's – 18" x 6"
Value: $75

#634
Rack Sign
Circa 1940's – 24" x 10"
Value: $75

Tin Signs

#635
Rack Sign
Circa 1940's – 24" x 10"
Value: $75

#636
Rack Sign
Circa 1950's – 18"x 6"
Value: $50

#637
Rack Sign/Yellow Background
17" x 5"
Value: $45

#638
Rack Sign
1958-63 – 11" x 14"
Value: $45

#639
Rack Sign/Yellow Background
15½" x 10"
Value: $45

#640
Rack Sign
Circa 1950's – 22" x 11"
Value: $45

Tin Signs

#641
Canadian / Yellow Background
Circa 1940's – 59" x 35"
Value: $600

#642
Heavy Tin – Circa 1930's
40" x 22"
Value: $275

#643
Heavy Tin – Circa 1930's
40" x 22"
Value: $275

Tin Signs

#644
Aluminum
Circa 1940's – 14" x 3"
Value: $350

#645
Cooler Sign
Circa 19350's – 24" x 18"
Value: $225

#646
Window Corner Sign
Circa 1940's – 12" x 12"
Value: $185

#647
Window Corner Sign
Circa 1940's – 12" x 12"
Value: $185

#648
Mexican / Yellow Background
Circa 1940's – 18" x 40"
Value: $165

Tin Signs

#649
Heavy Tin – Circa 1940's
26" x 10"
Value: $150

#650
Yellow Background (Canadian)
Circa 1950's – 48" x 36"
Value: $150

#651
Light Blue Background
Circa 1940's – 30" x 24"
Value: $145

Tin Signs

#652
Circa 1950's – 50" x 36"
Value: $125

#653
Red, White, & Blue
Circa 1950's – 16" x 48"
Value: $125

#654
Yellow Background
Circa 1950's – 18" x 44"
Value: $100

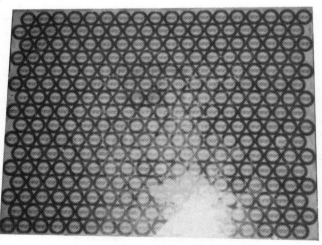

#655
Sheet of uncut bottle caps
Circa 1930's – 24" x 16"
Value: $95

Tin Signs

#656
Yellow Background
Circa 1950's — 18"x 44"
Value: $90

#657
Yellow Background
Circa 1960's — 18" x 44"
Value: $80

#658
Sheet of uncut bottle caps
Circa 1940's — 16" x 24"
Value: $75

#659
Yellow
Circa 1950's — 30" x 10"
Value: $75

#661
Yellow Background
Circa 1950's — 30" x 10"
Value: $55

#660
Yellow Background
Circa 1958-63 — 18" x 44"
Value: $80

Tin Signs

#662
Red, White & Blue
Circa 1950's – 31" x 27"
Value: $55

#663
Yellow Background/Self-Framed
Circa 1950's – 36" x 36"
Value: $65

#664
Yellow Background
Circa 1950's – 30" x 10"
Value: $55

#665
Tin over Cardboard,
Yellow Background
Circa 1950's – 11" x 9"
Value: $25

Wooden Signs

#666
Heavy Plywood
Circa 1930's – 48" x 11½"
Value: $900

#667
Masonite 2-Sided Flange
Circa 1950's – 12" Diameter
Value: $125

#668
2 Sided Flange (Masonite)
Circa 1940's – 12" Diameter
Value: $175

#669
Composition
1976 – 24" x 12"
Value: $25

#670
Masonite Rack Sign
Circa 1950's – 23" x 18"
Value: $95

Smoking Paraphernalia

#671
Sterling Silver Presentation
Cigarette Box
Circa 1960's – 6" x 3" x 1½"
Value: $450

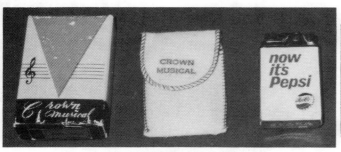

#672
Musical Lighter (2 Views)
with Box and Bag
Circa 1960's – 2" x 3"
Value: $125

#673
Tin Ashtray
Circa 1940's – 3¾" Diameter
Value: $95

#674
Musical Lighter (2 Views)
Circa 1950's – 2" x 3"
Value: $95

#675
Ceramic Ashtray
Circa 1950's – 4" Diameter
Value: $95

Smoking Paraphernalia

#676
Metal Ashtray with Plastic Bottle
Circa 1950's
5" Diameter 2½" Tail
Value: $85

#677
Metal Bottle Lighter with Box
Circa 1950's – 2"
Value: $75

#678
Glass Ashtray
Circa 1940's – 5" x 3"
Value: $85

#679
Glass Ashtray
Circa 1940's – 4" x 4"
Value: $75

#680
Glass Ashtray
Circa 1940's – 4" x 4"
Value: $75

#681
Glass Ashtray
Circa 1940's – 4" x 4"
Value: $85

#682
Metal Table Lighter
Circa 1950's
2½" x 2½" x 1½"
Value: $75

#683
Metal Lighter
Circa 1950's – 2½" x 1½"
Value: $45

#684
Tin Ashtray (2 Views)
Circa 1950's – 4" Diameter
Value: $40

#685
Tin Ashtray (2 Views)
Circa 1950's – 3¾" Diameter
Value: $35

Smoking Paraphernalia

#686
Tin Ashtray (Mexican)
Circa 1950's – 4" Diameter
Value: $45

#687
Glass Ashtray
1963 – 4" x 4"
Value: $25

#688
Metal Bottle Lighter
Circa 1950's – 2"
Value: $35

#689
Plastic Bottle Lighter
Circa 1950's – 2"
Value: $25

#690
Metal Lighter
Circa 1950's – 1½" x 2½"
Value: $30

#691
Metal Lighter
Circa 1960's – 2" x 3"
Value: $30

#692
Metal Lighter
Circa 1960's – 2" x 3"
Value: $30

Smoking Paraphernalia

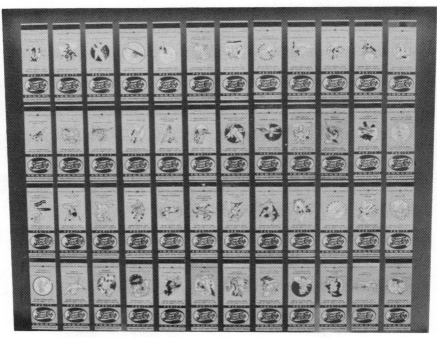

#693
Complete set of Disney Matchbooks
Circa 1940's
Value: $650 (Complete Set)

#694
Large Matchbook
Circa 1930's – 3½" x 5"
Value: $35

#695
Matchbook
Circa 1930's
Value: $30

#696
Matchbook
Circa 1930's
Value: $30

Smoking Paraphernalia

#697
Matchbook (Peru)
Circa 1930's
Value: $25

#698
Matchbook
Circa 1940's
Value: $25

#699
Matchbook (Spanish)
Circa 1930's
Value: $20

#700
Matchbook
Circa 1940's
Value: $20

#701
Matchbook
Circa 1930's
Value: $20

#702
Matchbook
Circa 1930's
Value: $15

Smoking Paraphernalia

#703
Matchbook
Circa 1940's
Value: $15

#704
Matchbook
Circa 1970's
Value: $5

#705
Matchbook
Circa 1960's
Value: $10

#706
Evervess Matchbook
Circa 1950's
Value: $10

#707
Evervess Matchbook
Circa 1940's
Value: $15

Straws and Straw Boxes

#708
Cardboard
Circa 1940's – 4" x 12" x 4"
Value: $225

#709
Cardboard
Circa 1950's – 4" x 12" x 4"
Value: $125

#710
Cardboard
Circa 1940's – 4" x 12" x 4"
Value: $225

#711
Cardboard
Circa 1940's – 4" x 13" x 3"
Value: $250

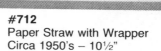

#712
Paper Straw with Wrapper
Circa 1950's – 10½"
Value: $10

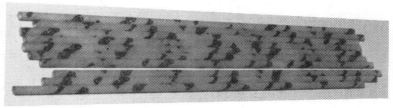

#713
Paper Straws
Circa 1950's – 10½"
Value: $5 each

Syrup Containers

#714
Tin
Circa 1960 – 1 Gallon
Value: $60

#715
Paper Label
Circa 1910 – 24 oz. Syrup Bottle
Value: $650

#716
Glass with Paper Label
Circa 1950's – 1 Gallon
Value: $50

#717
Glass with A.C.L.
Circa 1958 – 1963
Value: $50

#718
Cardboard Box
Circa 1950's – 4 Gallon Glass Jugs
Value: $25

Tap Knobs

#719
Plastic (Insert)
Circa 1950's — 3¼" x 2¾"
Value: $45

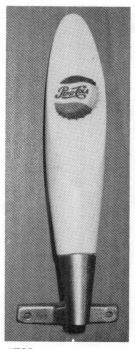

#720
Plastic and Metal
Circa 1950's — 2" x 10"
Value: $50

#721
Celluloid
Circa 1940's — 2¾" Diameter
Value: $125

#722
Plastic (insert) yellow background
Circa 1960's — 3¼" x 2¾"
Value: $35

#723
Lucite
Circa 1970's — 3" x 6"
Value: $15

#724
Lucite
Circa 1970's — 3" x 9"
Value: $15

#725
Plastic (insert)
Circa 1940's — 3¼" x 2¾"
Value: $75

Thermometers

#726
Reverse Glass Metal Frame
Circa 1930's – 10" x 22"
Value: $750

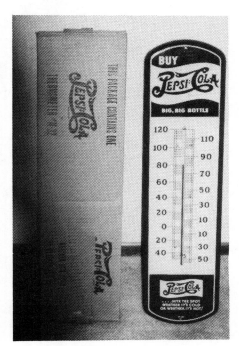

#727
Tin with Original Box
Circa 1940's – 7" x 27"
Value: $200 with box

#728
Tin with Original Box
Circa 1950 – 7" x 27"
Value: $135 with Box

Thermometers

#729
Round Desktop Weighted
Circa 1950's – 2½" Diameter
Value: $75

#730
Round Desktop Weighted
Circa 1960's – 2½" Diameter
Value: $65

#731
Yellow Tin
Circa 1950's – 7" x 27"
Value: $45

Toy Trucks

#732
Plastic with Box
Circa 1940's – 12"
Value: $475

#733
Tin (Linemar)
Circa 1950's – 2"
Value: $225

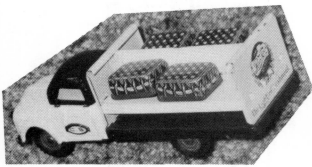

#734
Tin with Tin Cases
Circa 1950's – 6"
Value: $175

#735
Tin
Circa 1940's – 7"
Value: $125

#736
Tin
Circa 1950's – 12"
Value: $125

#737
Metal
Circa 1940's – 6"
Value: $150

Toys and Games

#738
Bicycle
Circa 1970's – 26"
Value: $175

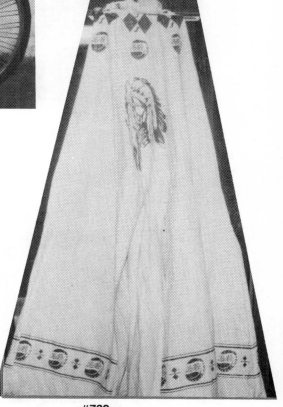

#739
Child's Teepee
Circa 1950's – 84" Tall
Value: $150

#740
Certificate and Badge
Circa 1940's – 12" x 12"
Value: $125 (set)

#741
Toy Refreshment Stand
Circa 1940's – 12" x 3" x 3"
Value: $150

Toys and Games

#743
Number Game
Circa 1930's – 3" x 5"
Value: $45

#742
Number Game with Envelope
Circa 1930's – 3" x 6"
Value: $85

#744
Toy Picnic Set (2 Views)
Circa 1950's – 8" x 12"
Value: $110

Toys and Games

#745
Bang Gun
Circa 1930's – 7" x 5"
Value: $110

#746
Cardboard Decoder
Circa 1958-1963 – 2" Diameter
Value: $65

#747
Marbles
Circa 1950's – 3" x 6"
Value: $65

#748
Sight Tester
Circa 1940's – 12" x 4"
Value: $35

#749
Toy Airplane
Circa 1940's – 8" x 6"
Value: $50

#750
Test Sight
Circa 1940's – 12" x 4"
Value: $35

#751
Plastic Bank
Circa 1960's – 36" Tall
Value: $50

Toys and Games

#752
Trivia Game
1986 – 14" x 10" x 3"
Value: $35

#753
500 Piece Puzzle
Circa 1960's – 12" x 10" Box
Value: $30

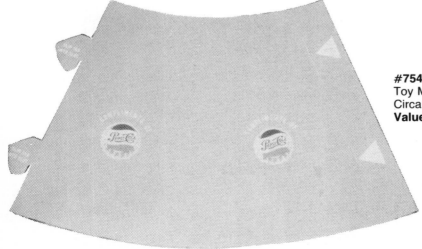

#754
Toy Megaphone
Circa 1950's – 16" x 12"
Value: $30

Toys and Games

#755
Stuffed Mrs. Santa Figure
Circa 1970's – 18"
Value: $30

#756
Stuffed Snowman Figure
Circa 1970's – 20"
Value: $30

#757
Stuffed Caroller Figure
Circa 1970's – 30"
Value: $30

#758
Set of Four Stuffed Figures
Circa 1970's – 18" x 20"
Value: $125 Set

#759
Stuffed Santa Figure
Circa 1960's – 14"
Value: $45

Toys and Games

#760
Kaleidoscope
Circa 1970's – 3" x 6"
Value: $20

#761
Baseball Cards
Circa 1960's – 4" x 8"
Value: $15 each

#762
Yo-Yo
Circa 1970's – 3" Diameter
Value: $15

#763
Tin Bank
Circa 1970's – 3" x 6"
Value: $10

#764
Walking Can
Circa 1970's – 3" x 8"
Value: $25

#765
Board Game
Circa 1970's – 19" x 10"
Value: $55

Trash Cans

#766
Metal – Circa 1960's
14" Diameter x 34" Tall
Value: $200

#767
Metal – Circa 1970's
14" Diameter x 34" Tall
Value: $125

#768
Plastic – Circa 1970's
13" x 24" x 17"
Value: $25

#769
Metal Circa 1950's
14" Diameter x 34" Tall
Value: $150

Vending Machines

#770
Electric
Circa 1950's
Value: $475

#771
Electric
Circa 1950's
Value: $325

Vending Machines

#772
Electric
Circa 1960's
Value: $225

#773
Electric
1950
Value: $350

#774
Electric
Circa 1960's
Value: $250

#775
Pocket Mirror
Circa 1900's – 1½" x 2½"
Value: $3000

Miscellaneous

#776
Bottle Hanger with enclosed recipe book
(2 Views) — Circa 1930's
3" x 12"
Value: $175

#777
Metal Bottle Mould
Circa 1958-1963
4½" x 8½" each
Value: $275

now
it's Pepsi...
perfect
anytime!

#778
Artist proof of sign #406 Vol. I
Circa 1960's — 18" x 24"
Value: $125

50 GROSS
KEEP DRY

STORE IN
COOL, DRY
PLACE

CROWNS

PEPSI-COLA COMPANY — LONG ISLAND CITY, N.Y.

#779
Bottle Cap Box
Circa 1940's — 50 Gross
Value: $65

Miscellaneous

#780
Christmas Card (2 Views)
Circa 1957 – 5" x 7"
Value: $45

#781
Bedroom Set
Circa 1960's
Value: $85 Set

Miscellaneous

#782
Pencil Clip
Circa 1910's — ¾" Diameter
Value: $85

#783
Pencil Clip
Circa 1940's — ¾" Diameter
Value: $40

#784
Pencil Clip
Circa 1940's — ¾" Diameter
Value: $40

#785
Pencil Clip
Circa 1950's — ¾" Diameter
Value: $10

#786
Bottle Cap
Circa 1930's — 1" Diameter
Value: $10

#787
Bottle Cap
Circa 1930's — 1" Diameter
Value: $10

#788
Evervess Bottle Cap
Circa 1940's — 1" Diameter
Value: $10

#789
Bottle Cap
Circa 1940's — 1" Diameter
Value: $5

#790
Bottle Cap
Circa 1940's — 1" Diameter
Value: $5

#791
Bottle Cap
Circa 1940's — 1" Diameter
Value: $5

Miscellaneous

#792
Playing Cards (Johnny Bench)
1970's
Value: $50

#793
Playing Cards (Joe Morgan)
1970's
Value: $50

#794
Playing Cards (Red)
1940's
Value: $85

#795
Playing Card Box
Circa 195 's – 6" x 4"
Value: $65

Miscellaneous

#796
Serving Tray
Circa 1960's – 14" Diameter
Value: $55

#797
Serving Tray
Circa 1970's – 14" Diameter
Value: $75

#798
Serving Tray
Circa 1970's – 11" x 14
Value: $35

#799
Transistor Radio with original box
Circa 1950's – 8" x 12"
Value: $325

Miscellaneous

#800
Bank Bag (White and Black)
Circa 1950's – 10" x 18"
Value: $15

#801
Bank Bag (Tan and Black)
Circa 1950's – 10" x 18"
Value: $15

#802
Vinyl Bag
Circa 1980's – 8" x 5"
Value: $5

#803
License Plate
1970's – 12" x 6"
Value: $5

#804
License Plate
1940's – 12" x 6"
Value: $75

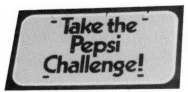

#805
License Plate
1970's – 12" x 6"
Value: $5

Miscellaneous

#806
Plant Souvenir (2 Views)
Circa 1958 – 2½" Diameter
Value: $45

#807
Paper Bookmarks
Circa 1940's – 3" x 12"
Value: $35 each

#808
Book Cover
Circa 1950's – 22" x 16"
Value: $35

#809
Locker Tag
Circa 1920's – 2" x 1"
Value: $35

#810
Iron-On
Circa 1930's – 2" x 2"
Value: $45

#811
Plastic Membership Card
Circa 1970's – 3" x 1½"
Value: $5

#812
Carton Hanger
Circa 1960's – 3" x 6"
Value: $10

Miscellaneous

#813
Postcard Frank Torre
1950's – 5" x 3"
Value: $40

#814
Postcard
1940's – 5" x 3"
Value: $45

#815
Fold Out Menu
Circa 1950's – 9" x 12"
Value: $30

#816
Menu Insert
Circa 1940's – 8½" x 11"
Value: $35

#817
Fold Out Menu (2 Views)
Circa 1960's – 9" x 12"
Value: $30

Miscellaneous

#818
Business Card
Circa 1940's – 3" x 1½"
Value: $20

#819
Cardboard Coaster
Circa 1950's – 3" Diameter
Value: $15

#820
Business Card
Circa 1940's – 3" x 1½"
Value: $20

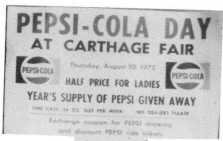

#821
Carton Insert
1972 – 4" x 4½"
Value: $10

#822
Box Knife
Circa 1970's – 4" x 1"
Value: $10

#823
Postcard Miss Pepsi (2 Views)
1960's – 5" x 3"
Value: $25

#824
75th Anniversary Owens, Inc.
Circa 1970's – 11" x 11"
Value: $75

#825
Plastic
Recent – 16" Diameter
Value: $35

#826
Pepsi and Pete Pillow
1970's – 24" x 18"
Value: $75

#827
Wood Peppermill
1973 – 2½"x 8"
Value: $45

#828
China Plate (2 Views Shown)
1980's – 8" Diameter
Value: $65

#829
Glass Sign
Recent – 14" x 28"
Value: $25

#830
Ceramic Statue
Recent – 12"
Value: $20

#831
Glass Front Clock
Recent – 8" x 18"
Value: $25

#832
Glasses (Set of 4)
1979 – 12 oz.
Value: $25 Set

#833
Wooden Thermometer
Recent – 8" x 24"
Value: $20

#835
Glass Sign
Recent – 24" x 12"
Value: $25

#834
Paper Sign
Recent – 14" x 24"
Value: $15

#836
Music Box
1970's – 14" Tall
Value: $45

New

#837
Quilt
Recent – Double Bed
Value: One of a kind

#838
Glass Sign
Recent – 16" x 24"
Value: $35

#839
Disneyland Paperweight
1972 – 2¾" x 5¼"
Value: $75

#840
Cloth Apron
Recent – 16" x 22"
Value: $15

#841
Tin
Recent – 4" x 8"
Value: $5